Aileen Williams.

GW00394285

Violin Grade 1

Pieces

for Trinity College London examinations

2010-2015

Published by:
Trinity College London
4th floor, 89 Albert Embankment
London SE1 7TP UK

T +44 (0)20 7820 6100
F +44 (0)20 7820 6161
E music@trinitycollege.co.uk
www.trinitycollege.co.uk

Registered in England
Company no. 02683033
Charity no. 1014792

Music processed by New Notations London and Moira Roach.
Printed in England by the Halstan Printing Group, Amersham, Bucks.

Gopak

no. 5 from *Travel Tunes*

Margery Dawe

[Lively ♩ = 92–112]

Hornpipe

from *Little Suite no. 3*

Peter Martin

(*1*) **rit.** and pause on D.S. only.

Fiddler's Fancy

Sheila Nelson

(*1*) The repeat must be played in the examination.

This piece may be played unaccompanied in the examination.

Jumping Jive

Christine Myers

Morning Song

Robert Trory and Sally Mays

All Mixed Up!

Mary Cohen

The words should be omitted in the examination.

Valsette

Margery Dawe

Down by the Salley Gardens

Traditional Irish

Corfu and Cefalonia

arr. Edward Huw Jones

Traditional

Sailing

Robert Trory and Sally Mays